Fredericka's Name

By
Evangeline Nicholas

Illustrated By
Charlen Satrom

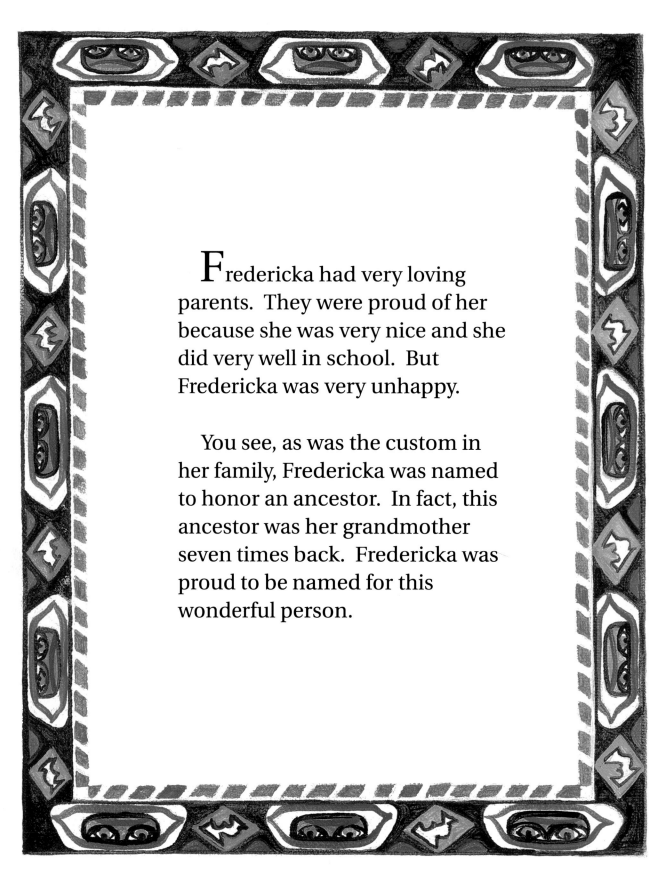

Fredericka had very loving parents. They were proud of her because she was very nice and she did very well in school. But Fredericka was very unhappy.

You see, as was the custom in her family, Fredericka was named to honor an ancestor. In fact, this ancestor was her grandmother seven times back. Fredericka was proud to be named for this wonderful person.

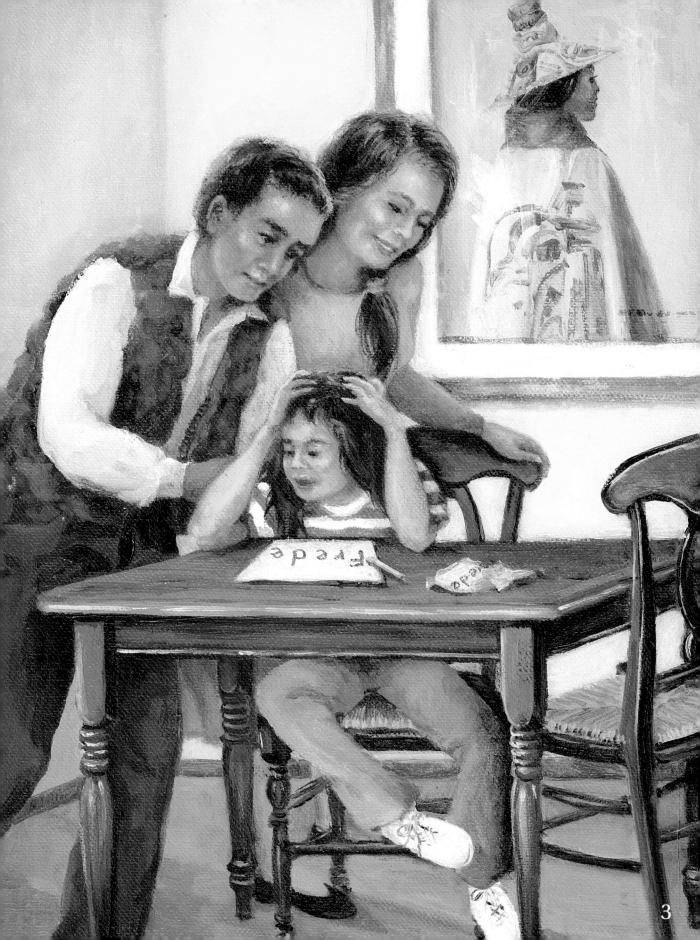

Her parents told Fredericka stories about her seven-times-back grandmother who could heal the sick. This honored grandmother had also helped teach many things to the children in her lifetime.

5

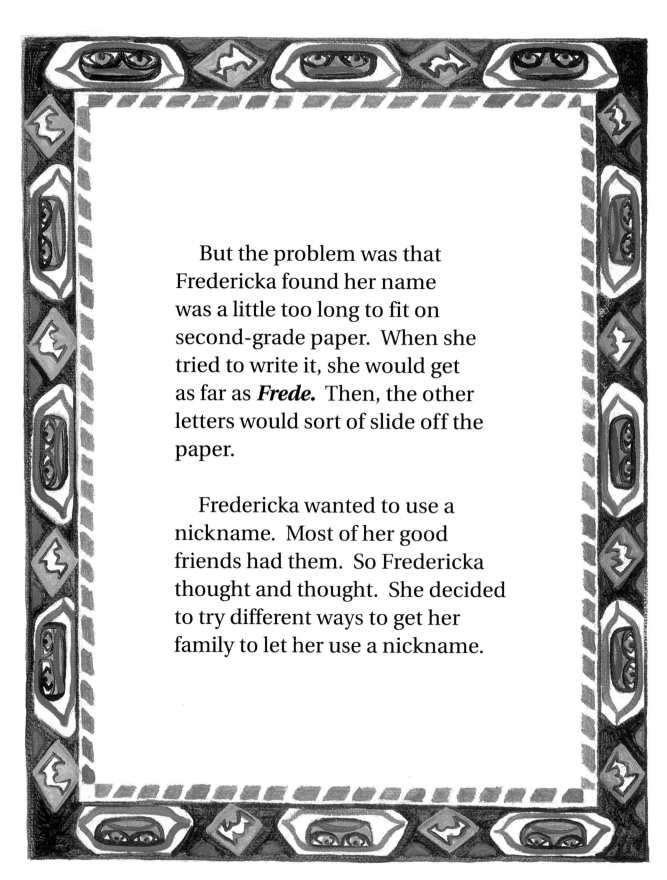

But the problem was that Fredericka found her name was a little too long to fit on second-grade paper. When she tried to write it, she would get as far as **Frede.** Then, the other letters would sort of slide off the paper.

Fredericka wanted to use a nickname. Most of her good friends had them. So Fredericka thought and thought. She decided to try different ways to get her family to let her use a nickname.

2nd Grade Picture Stories

We have a new puppy. nam... Tony

Mother and I went shopping ... fun. Liz

A long time ago my Grandma had a Potlach. Freda

...wish I was ...so I ...could fly. Zack

I have a red bike. It goes fast. Gwen

At school, when the class tie-dyed T-shirts, Fredericka put **Icka** on hers.

At a Brownie-troop meeting, Fredericka printed **Frede** on her backpack.

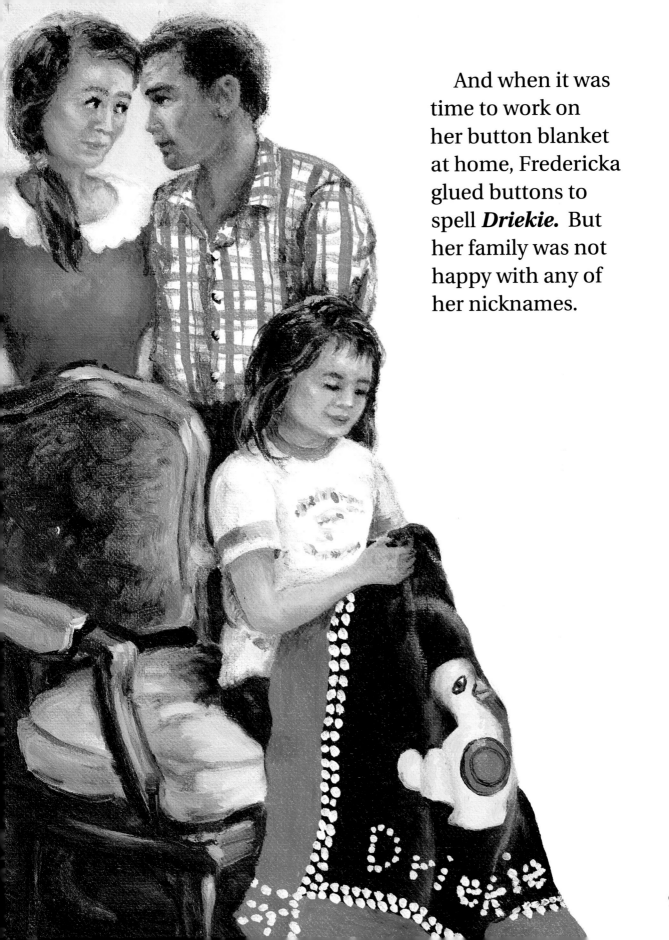

And when it was time to work on her button blanket at home, Fredericka glued buttons to spell *Driekie.* But her family was not happy with any of her nicknames.

9

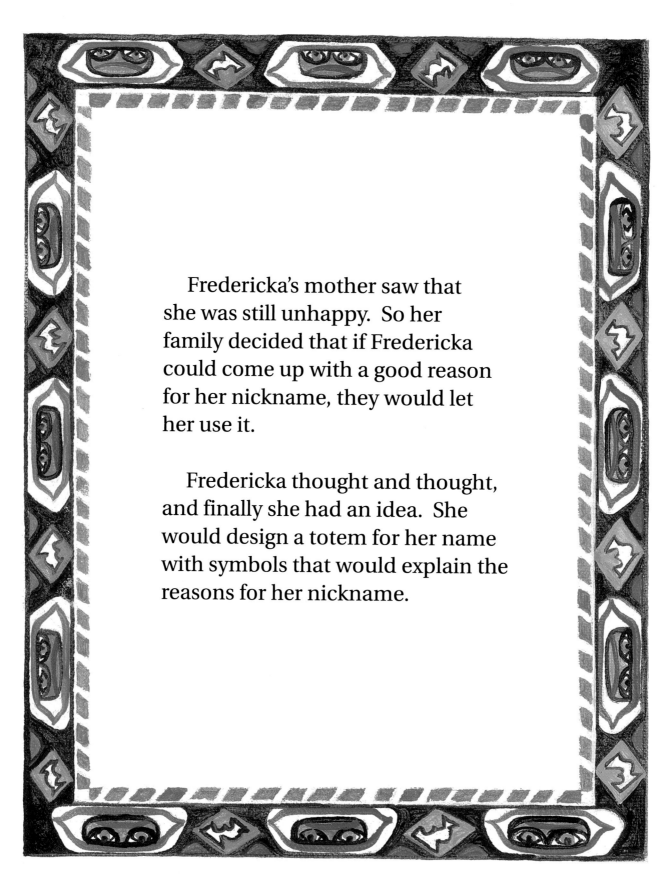

Fredericka's mother saw that she was still unhappy. So her family decided that if Fredericka could come up with a good reason for her nickname, they would let her use it.

Fredericka thought and thought, and finally she had an idea. She would design a totem for her name with symbols that would explain the reasons for her nickname.

11

This is how she thought the totem and nickname should look.

D for dancing girl

R for being really responsible

I for ice cream, a favorite snack

E for early morning riser

K for kindness to animals

I for inthusiastic

E for easily making friends

13

Fredericka's mother and father were really proud of her. They thought that her totem was well-done and that she had good reasons for her nickname.

So after Fredericka's mother helped her correct *inthusiastic* to *enthusiastic*, everyone agreed that she could use **Driekee** for her nickname.

Fredericka still has to write her full name on her papers at school. But everyone knows that it will get easier as she passes from grade to grade. But Fredericka just loves it when her family and friends admire her totem and call her **Driekee.**